THE LITTLE BOOK OF

JULIA ALGORITHMS

Typeset in Franklin Gothic Book, Julia Mono & Courier New

Cover illustration: Pentachorons by Cormullion

ISBN: 978-1-8381736-0-9

Acknowledgements

Thanks first of all to the Julia Community for creating an amazing language that is fun to code in and for making all newcomers feel welcome.

Thanks to Jeff Bezanson for his kindness in writing a brilliant foreword.

Thanks to Subbarao Manchala for his detailed feedback on an early draft that made the book so much better.

And finally, thanks to my parents for their constant support and encouragement.

CONTENTS

FOREWORD

Like the author of the Julia edition of this book, I started programming at a very young age.

The Apple II's square cursor blinked at me expectantly.

I typed something.

It beeped and said: "?SYNTAX ERROR".

I typed something else, with much the same result.

Needless to say, I was hooked — was there any way to get it to say something other than "syntax error"? — but I needed a book like this one.

Today, many of the frustrations of programming are the same. But a lot has improved: aside from the technology getting better, programming language development has become an open, participatory event. Once you get the hang of writing programs in Julia, see if you can think of ways to improve the language itself, or its ecosystem of packages. For example, try making your own game with GameZero.jl, and the improving the package for everybody, as the author of this book has done.

I am grateful to Ahan for expanding the resources available to help open this path.

Jeff Bezanson

Cambridge, MA, September 2020

PREFACE

Many see coding as a mystery-shrouded, magical skill that takes years to learn even the basics. Of course, as with any skill, practice is necessary, but it isn't more difficult to learn than anything else.

I first learnt coding when I was 7, and since, I have learnt multiple languages. I wanted to prove that it is something that anyone can learn, no matter their age. And so I wrote this book. Primarily aimed at beginners to coding, it teaches you how to code in the Julia programming language.

Originally, this book was written by William Lau to aid in the learning of Python for secondary school students. A lot of the credit for the interesting challenges and explanations should go to him. I am so grateful for his permission in writing a Julia version of his book.

This book is a workbook, that demonstrates basic programming principles and then checks understanding with challenges. Solutions to these can be found in the back of the book.

Do not worry if you have written an alternative solution. Also be aware that these solutions were not produced by typing the whole program out and running them with no syntax and logic errors on the first time! There was a debugging process as I wrote each line or block of code. Encountering errors whilst iteratively testing is the "normal" way to develop programs.

All the code for this book is available in the GitHub repository

https://github.com/SquidSinker/littlebookofalgorithms.jl

Ahan Sengupta

London, September 2020

LOWEST NUMBER

A program which takes two numbers as inputs and outputs the smallest number.

When you first started programming, you may have produced a program to ouput a lower number without using functions.

```
1   println("Enter the first number: ")
2   num1 = parse(Int, readline())
3   println("Enter the second number: ")
4   num2 = parse(Int, readline())
5
6   if num1 <= num2
7       lowest = num1
8   else
9       lowest = num2
10  end
11
12  println("The lowest number is ", lowest)
```

- Lines 2 & 4: The user input is read from the terminal as a string, and the parse function converts in to an integer.

This code uses what is known as an 'if statement'. This is used to check conditions and will run the code inside it if the condition returns 'true'.

Write an if statement checking if the variable 'x' is between 4 and 7.

if _____ && _____

LOWEST NUMBER CONTINUED...

However, good programmers write code which can be reused and tested in isolation (known as unit testing). Therefore, using a subroutine (also known as a function) to create a function would produce a "better" program that is modular. In Julia, a function is defined using the function keyword. Within parentheses, the parameters (or arguments) of the function are declared. When the function is called, the parameters are passed in. Within the function, the parameters are available as variables.

Whilst the use of a function in the second program allows you to call the function multiple times in the main program, it does not allow for full code re-use.

```
1   function lower_num(num1, num2)
2       if num1 <= num2
3           lowest = num1
4       else
5           lowest = num2
6       end
7       println("The lowest number is ", lowest)
8   end
9
10  println("Enter the first number: ")
11  first_num = parse(Int, readline())
12  println("Enter the second number: ")
13  second_num = parse(Int, readline())
14  lower_num(first_num, second_num)
```

LOWEST NUMBER CONTINUED...

...What happens if you wanted to use this lowest number later in the program? In this case, it makes sense to use a function that returns a value.

```
1   function lower_num(num1, num2)
2       if num1 <= num2
3           lowest = num1
4       else
5           lowest = num2
6       end
7       println("The lowest number is ", lowest)
8   end
9
10  println("Enter the first number: ")
11  first_num = parse(Int, readline())
12  println("Enter the second number: ")
13  second_num = parse(Int, readline())
14
15  lowest = lower_num(first_num, second_num)
16
17  println("The lowest number is ", lowest)
```

- The function `lower_num` is defined on lines 1-8. We have to define functions before we can call (use) them.
- Usage of the function is demonstrated on lines 10-17. We still take two numbers as integer inputs on Lines 8-9.
- Line 11 calls the function `lower_num` with two arguments: the contents of `first_num` and `second_num` variables. These arguments are passed into the parameters `num1` and `num2` respectively[1]. The result is stored in the variable `lowest`.

[1] Arguments and parameters should have different names even if they seem to serve the same purpose. In this case both `num1` and `first_num` store the first number. However, the variable `first_num` has global scope, it can be accessed and changed anywhere in the program. The parameter `num1` has local scope, it is a local variable which can only be accessed in the function.

CHALLENGE 1: HIGHEST NUMBER

Write a function that takes three numbers — num1, num2 and num3 — and returns the highest.

```
function highest_number(num1, num2, num3)
    if num1 >= num2 && num1 >= num3
```

CHALLENGE 2: CALLING HIGHEST NUMBER

Complete the program below which asks the user to enter three integers and then calls the `highest_number` function from the previous page. The returned value is stored in a variable called `highest` and then output as a meaningful message.

```
println("Enter the first number")
num1_in = parse(Int, readline())
println("Enter the second number")
num2_in = parse(Int, readline())
println("Enter the third number")
num3_in = parse(Int, readline())


highest = highest_number(_____)


print("The highest number was _____)
```

CHALLENGE 3: OPTIONS

Complete the function below. The function has a parameter called `num` which takes a number as an argument and returns a subject. These numbers correspond to the following subjects:

1 Computer Science
2 Music
3 Dance
4 PE

If the student passes any other value into num, it should return "Error"

```
function options(_____)
        if num == 1
                return "Computer Science"
        elseif num == 2
                return "Music"
```

CHALLENGE 4: CALLING OPTIONS

Write a program which calls the function `options` from Challenge 3. The user should be prompted to enter a number to choose a subject option. The program should then output a meaningful confirmation message based on the user's input.

CHALLENGE 5: TRACING IF STATEMENTS

Q1) State the output for the following program when the program is run four times with four different inputs:

num_in	Ouput
8	8
3	
12	
5	

```
1   function mystery_number(num)
2       if num < 5
3           println(8)
4       elseif num < 3
5           println(8)
6       elseif num == 3
7           println(3)
8       else
9           println(num)
10      end
11  end
12
13  println("Enter a number: ")
14  num_in = parse(Int, readline())
15  mystery_number(num_in)
```

Q2) In the program above, four lines of code are redundant i.e. they can be removed without affecting the program's output, which four lines can be removed:

Q3) Lines 6 and 7 state that when the number 3 is passed in, the output should be 3. However, this does not work, explain why:

CHALLENGE 6: REFINING

Re-write the program from the previous page so that the program outputs 1 if the value of num is 3. It should output 8 if the number is less than 5 (but not 3). It should output the number entered for all other cases.

Hint: You will need to re-order the if statement.

CHALLENGE 7: PARSON'S PUZZLE

Parson's puzzles are named after Dale Parsons[1]. To solve the puzzle, re-arrange the code blocks into the correct order. The function should take two numbers as arguments and subtract the smallest number from the largest. The result is returned.

A
```
println("Enter a number")
num1_in = parse(Int, readline())
println("Enter a number")
num2_in = parse(Int, readline())

difference = num1_in - num2_in

println("The difference is ", difference)
```

B
```
function subtract(num1, num2)
```

C
```
    return out
end
```

D
```
    else
        out = num2 - num1
    end
```

E
```
    if num1 > num2
        out = num1 - num2
```

Correct order:

[1]Keen students may think that there is a misplaced apostrophe here. However, in Parsons' original paper co-authored with Patricia Haden in 2006, they are referred to as "Parson's puzzles". Some refer to them as "Parsons problems" or simply "Parsons".

CHALLENGE 8: MULTIPLE CHOICE QUESTIONS

Circle the correct answer(s) to the questions below.

1) How is a value returned from a function?:

A. Using the `return` keyword

B. Last computed value

C. As an input parameter

D. TODO

2) The condition below can be translated as:

`if num1 > 9`

A. If num1 is greater than or equal to 9

B. If 9 is greater than num1

C. If num1 is greater than 9

D. If num1 is less than 9

3) Values passed into parameters are known as:

A. Variables

B. Functions

C. Arguments

D. Integers or Strings

4) What is the keyword used to define a function in Julia:

A. function

B. define

C. sub

D. def

STRING CONCATENATION: MAKING A USERNAME

A function which outputs a username based on a student's first name, surname and year of enrolment.

E.g. Joseph Campbell 2015 should return 15JCampbell.

```
1   function username(forename, surname, year)
2       username_out = year[3:4] * forename[1] * last_name
3
4       println("Your username is " * username_out)
5   end
6
7   println("Enter your first name: ")
8   first_name = readline()
9   println("Enter your surname: ")
10  last_name = readline()
11  println("Enter the year you joined the school: ")
12  joined = readline()
13
14  username(first_name, last_name, joined)
```

- The function `user_name` is defined on lines 1-4.
- Line 2: Strings can be sliced, with the first index being 1. In this case for the year, we start at 3 and stop at 4 (inclusive). This means we would slice year[3] and year[4] i.e. the last two digits of the `year`. These are concatenated (using '*') with the first letter from the `forename` and the entire `surname`.
- Lines 7-9: This shows how the function might be used. First the user's details are taken as string inputs .
- Then the function is called on line 14 with the user's details as arguments.
- The output is shown below:

```
Enter your first name: Joseph
Enter your surname: Campbell
Enter the year you joined the school: 2015
Your username is 15JCampbell
```

STRING CONCATENATION: MAKING A USERNAME CONTINUED...

If you wanted to use this `user_name` function later to generate an email address, this would not be possible without duplication of code, it is therefore wise to rewrite this function to return a value. This is shown below:

```
1   function username(forename, surname, year)
2       username_out = year[3:4] * forname[1] * last_name
3       return username_out
4   end
5
6   function main()
7       println("Enter your first name: ")
8       first_name = readline()
9       println("Enter your surname: ")
10      last_name = readline()
11      println("Enter the year you joined the school: ")
12      year = readline()
13
14      gen_user_name = username(first_name, last_name, year)
15      println("Your username is " * gen_user_name)
16  end
17
```

Here we introduce a programming convention of placing your main program in a main function. The main function should be the only function which contains inputs and ouputs in the entire program. From this main function you should call other functions, passing arguments into parameters. This process is known as parameter passing.

The main function above spans lines 6-17.

CHALLENGE 9: INITIALS ONLY

Write a function that takes three strings as arguments: a first name, a middle name and a last name. The program should take these three arguments and return only the first letter of each string thereby generating initials.

```
function initials_only(first, middle, last)

    initials =


    return
```

CHALLENGE 10: SUBJECT SHORTENER

On school timetables, subjects are often shortened to their first 3 characters e.g. Maths becomes Mat, French becomes Fre and Music becomes Mus.

Write a function that has a parameter called subject, and returns the shortened subject name.

CALCULATE THE AREA OF A CIRCLE

A function which calculates the area of a circle.

```
1   CONSTANT_PI = 3.14159
2
3   function circle_area(radius_in)
4       area_out = CONSTANT_PI * radius_in ^ 2
5       return area_out
6   end
7
8   println("Enter the radius of the circle: ")
9   radius = parse(Int, readline())
10  area = circle_area(radius)
11  println("The area of the circle is $(area)")
```

- Line 1: As the value of Pi *will not change whilst the program is running*, this is a constant. Programmers sometimes write constants in capitals and may give them meaningful names as shown.
- Line 3: The function `circle_area` is defined and has one parameter (a placeholder/variable) called `radius_in`.
- The `area_out` is calculated radius ^ 2 may also be written as radius ** 2 in other languages.
- Lines 8-11: This shows how the function may be used.
- Line 10: The `circle_area` is called and the `radius` is passed as an argument. The result is stored in the variable `area`.
- Line 11: In Julia, we can also use a dollar sign to concatenate the `area` to the output message. The advantage of using a dollar sign to concatenate is that conversion of a number to a string is done automatically.

CHALLENGE 11: VOLUME OF A CUBOID

Write a function that takes the length, width and height as arguments and return the volume of the cuboid.

Then call the function to output an answer with a meaningful message.

CHALLENGE 12: ADD

Write a function called `add` which has two parameters, `num1` and `num2`, which are then added together and returned to the user.

```
function add (num1,num2)



end


println("Enter a number")
num1_in =
println("Enter another number")
num2_in =


total = add(num1_in, num2_in)


println("The sum of the two numbers is
", total)
```

CHALLENGE 13: MULTIPLE CHOICE QUESTIONS

Circle the correct answer to the questions below.

1) What is the output of the following:
```
name = "Shenaz"
print(name[3:5])
```
A.   345
B.   ena
C.   na
D.   naz

2) What is the output of the following:
```
subject = "Computer Science"
print(subject[1])
```
A.   C
B.   o
C.   1
D.   Co

3) What is the result of 2^3?
A.   6
B.   23
C.   2^3
D.   8

4) What is a constant?
A.   A variable which stays the same whilst the program is running
B.   A value which can not change whilst the program is running
C.   A numerical value
D.   Part of a formula which is defined

ODD OR EVEN?

A function which checks if a number is odd or even. It will print a meaningful message accordingly. The program should loop until the user enters the sentinel value "STOP"

```
1   function is_odd(num)
2       if num % 2 == 0
3           return "even"
4       else
5           return "odd"
6       end
7   end
8
9   while true
10      println("Enter a number or STOP to finish")
11      number = readline()
12
13      if number != "STOP"
14          number = parse(Int, number)
15          odd = is_odd(number)
16          println(odd)
18      else
19          break
20      end
21  end
```

- Line 2: The % symbol in Julia calculates the remainder from a division. In this case, we are calculating for the remainder when dividing by 2. This can also be called using the `rem(x,y)` function.
- Line 9: Infinite loop.
- Lines 13-14: Provided the user does not enter the sentinel value (also known as a rogue or trip value) of "STOP", the while loop will continue to call `is_odd` with each new number inputted to check if it is odd or even.
- Line 16: If the user enters the sentinel value, the keyword `break` forces the while loop to stop.

CHALLENGE 14: ODD OR EVEN FUNCTION

The Odd or Even program could be improved. Re-write the program so that all inputs and outputs take place inside of another function.

CHALLENGE 15: IS X A MULTIPLE OF Y

Use % to write a function which tells us if a given number x is a multiple of y.

E.g. if x is 18 and y is 9, the function should output a meaningful message to tell us that 18 is a multiple of 9. If x is 20 and y is 7, the function should output a meaningful message to tell us 20 is not a multiple of 7.

```
                    is_multiple (x_in,          )
_____
     if                              == 0
         _____
         println(_____)

     else

         println(     , "is not a multiple of",    )
                 ____                              ___
end


print("A program to check if x is a multiple of
y")

println("Enter a number to see if it is a mul-
tiple")

x = parse(Int, readline())

println("Enter a number to divide by")

y = parse(Int, readline())

#Call the function, passing in x and y
```

CHALLENGE 16: TRACING WITH DIV

% returns the remainder from a division. We can also do integer division, also known as floor division by using the `div(x,y)` function or the ÷ symbol, which can be entered by typing `\div` <TAB>. Using ÷ ignores any remainder and always rounds down.

e.g. $10 ÷ 5 = 2$ (10 goes in 5 two times)

$10 ÷ 3 = 3$ (10 goes into 3 three times. we ignore the 1 remainder)

$4 ÷ 3 = 0$ (4 does not go into 3, we ignore the 4 remainder)

$3 ÷ 4 = 1$ (3 goes into 4 once, we ignore the 1 remainder)

1) State the output for the following program when the program is run four times with four different inputs:

num1	num2	Output
1	8	
3	9	
14	10	
21		4

```
function add_div(num1_in, num2_in)
    out = (num1_in + num2_in) ÷ 10
    return out
end

println("Enter your first number")
num1 = parse(Int, readline())
println("Enter your second number")
num2 = parse(Int, readline())

floor = add_div(num1, num2)
println(floor)
```

2) Calculate the following:

a) $21 ÷ 7 = $ _____

b) $9 ÷ 4 = $ _____

FOR LOOPS: OUTPUTTING NUMBERS

A function which outputs all the numbers between a certain start and stop value (inclusive).

Here we will use a for loop (also known as a count-controlled loop) as we know exactly how many times we want to loop based on the start and stop values.

```
1   function number_generator(start, stop)
2       for i in start:stop
3           println(i)
4       end
5   end
6
7   println("Enter a start value")
8   start_num = parse(Int, readline())
9   println("Enter a stop value")
10  stop_num = parse(Int, readline())
11
12  number_generator(start_num, stop_num)
```

- The function `number_generator` is defined on lines 1-5.
- Line 2: uses a for loop to iterate from the start value to the stop value. In Julia, the stop value is inclusive, so `number_generator(1,10)` would print numbers 1 to 10.
- Lines 7-10: The user's details are taken as inputs .
- Then the function is called on line 12.

WHILE LOOPS: NUMBER GUESSER

A program which generates a random number then asks the user to guess the random number. The program repeats until the correct number is guessed.

As we do not know how many guesses the user will need to guess the number correctly, we use a while loop (also known as a condition-controlled loop). In this case, our condition (`true`) causes it to be indefinite.

```
1    randomNumber = rand(1:10)
2
3    while true
4        println("Guess the number between 1 and 10")
5        guess = parse(Int, readline())
6        if guess == randomNumber
7            println("Correct")
8            break
9        else
10           println("Try again")
11       end
12   end
```

- Line 1: Initialise the random number the user is supposed to guess
- Unlike the previous program, we do not know how many times we need to repeat; the user could get the answer wrong 8 times or they could guess it first time. In these situations we use a conditional loop i.e. a while loop.
- Line 6-7: If the user's guess is correct, they will be informed and the while loop will end.
- Lines 9-10: If the user guess is incorrect, we return to the top of the loop i.e. line 3.

UNLIMITED PIN ATTEMPTS

A program which allows the user to enter a pin number. If the user gets the pin number wrong, they are prompted to enter the pin again.

N.B. An unlimited number of attempts is a bad idea as it allows for brute force hacking. However, this is a common algorithm that is used in guessing games e.g. guess the number.

```
1   while true
2       println("Please enter the pin")
3       pin = readline()
4       if pin == "1984"
5           println("Logged in")
6           break
7       else
8           println("Incorrect")
9       end
10  end
```

- The program keeps looping while the pin is not equal to 1984. It is very similar to the program on page 11.
- Line 1: Sets an initial value that is not equal to the pin. This ensures the while loop runs at least once.
- Line 3 asks the user to enter their pin.
- Lines 5-8 check to see if the pin matches, a meaningful message is produced depending on the outcome.

BASIC LOGIN SYSTEM

A program which checks to see if the username and password
matches the one in our program. The user gets three attempts.

```
1    username = "James"
2    password = "myPassword"
3    tries = 0
4
5    while tries < 3
6        println("Enter the username")
7        user_in = readline()
8        println("Enter the password")
9        pass_in = readline()
10
11       if user_in == username
12           if pass_in == password
13               println("Logged in")
14           else
15               println("Incorrect username or password")
16           end
17       else
18           println("Incorrect username or password")
19       end
20       global tries += 1
21   end
```

- Line 3: Initialises a while loop counter called `tries` to 0.
- Line 5: The while loop provides a maximum of 3 password
  attempts. We use a while loop because we do not know how
  many attempts the user will need to get the answer correct.
- Lines 11-15: If the correct `username` and `password` is
  supplied, we output a "logged in" message and the loop ends.
  Otherwise, a meaningful error message is shown and the `tries`
  variable is incremented (Line 20).
- Line 20: This is also a common way to increase a score or
  counter. The variable `tries` is declared in line 3 outside of the
  while loop and not in a function . In other words it has global
  scope. Therefore, it must be marked as a global variable to be
  incremented in the loop.

CHALLENGE 17: ACRONYM GENERATOR

Recall challenge 9 on page 17. The program works well for people with a first name, middle name and last name. However, some people do not have middle names and some people have more than one. In other scenarios, you may wish to simply generate some acronyms to shorten several words e.g. Joint Photographic Experts Group can be shortened to JPEG.

The program below should ask the user for a word and keep asking for words until "XXX" is entered. "XXX" acts as a sentinel value which stops a loop from running. When it is, the program should stop asking for words and an acronym should be generated.

```
sentinel = "XXX" #The sentinel value

acronym = ""

while true

    println("Enter a word or 'XXX' to finish")

    word = _____

  if word != sentinel

      acronym = acronym + word[    ]

  else

      break

  end

end

println(_____)
```

CHALLENGE 18: ACRONYM GENERATOR 2.0

The previous acronym generator program is inefficient as the user has to enter each word separately and has to enter a sentinel value.

Fill in the gaps in the program below to make a more efficient program which takes several words and generates an acronym based on the first character of each word.

N.B. in the program below we can iterate through each word in words_list by using the line `for word in words_list`

```
acronym = ""
println("Enter words to convert to acronym")
words = readline()
#Convert words into a list of individual words
words_list = split(words)
#For each word in the words_list
for word in words_list
    global acronym
    acronym = acronym * word[1]

println(_____)
```

CHALLENGE 19: ROLL A DOUBLE TO START

Write a program which simulates two dice being rolled. Output the values of both dice. Keep prompting the user to roll the dice until the two dice match e.g. Double 6. When the user rolls a double, output the message "Game loading". For all other combinations, ask the user to press Enter to roll again.

Remember, when we do not know how many times we need to run the loop, this is a conditional loop i.e. a while loop.

CHALLENGE 20: KEEPING SCORE OVER THREE ROUNDS

Write a program which simulates two dice being rolled three times. Output the total value of both dice for each roll. Keep track of the score over 3 rounds and output the total at the end

Hint: As we know that the pair of dice are rolled three times, this repetition is fixed. We therefore need to use a count-controlled loop i.e. a for loop.

LOWEST NUMBER IN AN ARRAY

A program outputs the lowest number of an array.

```
1   numbers_list = [9, 8, 7, 5, 6, 2, 1, 12, 14, 0 , 13]
2
3   lowest = numbers_list[1]
4
5   for i in numbers_list
6       global lowest
7       if i < lowest
8           lowest = i
9       end
10  end
11
12  println("The lowest number in the list is $(lowest)")
```

- Line 3: We start with the hypothesis that the item at position 1 of numbers_list is the lowest.
- Line 5: The for loop will loop as many times as elements in the array 'numbers_list', with i taking the value of the element of the array which corresponds to the current iteration of the for loop.
- Line 6: Variables must be global to be changed in a for loop but declared outside of it, and when not in a function.
- Lines 7-8 If the current value is smaller than lowest, this number replaces the item in lowest.
- Line 9: When the for loop has finished and we have therefore reached the end of the list, we output the value of lowest.

This can also be written as a function.

```
1   function find_lowest(numbers_list_in)
2       lowest = numbers_list_in[1]
3       for i in numbers_list_in
4           if i < lowest
5               lowest = i
6           end
7       end
8       return lowest
9   end
10
11  numbers_list = [9,8,7,5,6,2,1,12,14,0,13]
12  lowest_num = find_lowest(numbers_list)
13  println("The lowest number in the list is $(lowest_num)")
```

LINEAR SEARCH

Iterating through a array from start to finish as seen in the previous algorithm is effectively a linear search. We start at position 1 and continue checking each position from top to bottom until we reach the end. A meaningful message informs the user whether the item was found.

```
1   function linear_search(target)
2       names = ["Elizabeth", "Samuel", "Jawwad",
3               "Yacoub", "Cara", "Jess",
4               "Benji", "Thamber", "Suki", "Zi", "Q"]
5       found = false
6
7       for i in 1:length(names)
8           if target == names[i]
9               println("$(target) found at position $(i)")
10              found = true
11          end
12      end
13      if found == false
14          println("$(target) was not found")
15      end
16  end
17
18  println("Who are you searching for?")
19  name = readline()
20  linear_search(name)
```

- For all searching algorithms, you should start by setting a Boolean flag to `false`. We do this on line 4.
- Lines 7-11: If the target matches the item in the array, the name is outputted and the Boolean flag is set to `true`.
- Lines 13-14: When we've iterated through the entire list, check to see if `found` is still `false`. If so, the item was not in the list.
- Line 18: Notice how we pass the argument stored in the variable called `name` into the parameter called `target`. The argument and parameter name are different so that we understand that their scope is different.

CHALLENGE 21: HIGHEST NUMBER IN A ARRAY

Write a program which iterates through a array of numbers and outputs the highest number

```
numbers = [9, 8, 72, 22, 21, 81, 2, 1]
```

CHALLENGE 22: HIGHEST NUMBER IN A LIST FUNCTION

Re-write the program from the previous page as a function. The list of numbers should be passed in as an argument. The function should then iterate through a list of numbers and return the highest number

```
numbers = [9, 8, 72, 22, 21, 81, 2, 1]
```

CHALLENGE 23: WEAK PASSWORD?

Write a program which asks the user to enter a desired password. Perform a linear search through a array of obvious weak passwords. If the user's password is found in the obvious passwords list, output a message to tell them it is weak and would be easily hacked using a brute force attack.

```
obvious = ["password", "qwerty", "hello123",
"letmein", "123456"]
```

CHALLENGE 24: WEAK PASSWORD CONTINUED

Add in various validation checks to the program on the previous page. One example might be a length check, so if the password does not meet a particular length it is also declared weak. Other checks could be a presence check and format check. The format check could check to see if the user entered any numbers, symbols and a mixture of upper and lower case letters. Meaningful messages are necessary for each different validation check.

CHALLENGE 25: PENALTY SHOOTOUT

Write a program which simulates a penalty shootout. The computer is the goalkeeper and dives a random direction or stays in the centre each turn. The keeper's move is generated but not outputted at first. The user takes a penalty by typing in "left", "right" or "centre". The keeper's move is then outputted. If the player typed left and the keeper dives left, the penalty is saved etc. The program repeats 5 times. After 5 penalties, the winner is announced with a meaningful message.

```
keeper = ["left", "centre", "right"]
```

CHALLENGE 26: TRACING LOOPS

1) Write the values of x and y for the program below:

x	y
0	
1	

```
1    for x in 1:3
2          if x % 2 == 0
3               y = x + 2
4               println(y)
5          end
6    end
```

2) Re-write the for loop (line 1) below if we wanted the x value to loop from 1 to 10:

CHALLENGE 27: MULTIPLE CHOICE QUESTIONS

Circle the correct answer based on the following code:

```
for count in 1:5
    num1 = rand(1:10)
end
```

1) What are the highest and lowest possible values of num1?
A. 10 and 1
B. 10 and 0
C. 9 and 1
D. 9 and 0

2) What are the first and last values of count if they were outputted?
A. 0 and 5
B. 0 and 4
C. 1 and 5
D. 1 and 4

3) How many times does the for loop repeat?
A. 5 times
B. 0 times
C. 4 times
D. 6 times

4) Given a list called sentence which consists of 5 words, other than `for count in 1:5,` how else can you iterate through each word in the sentence?

TOTAL OF AN ARRAY

A program which adds up numbers in a array.

```
1 number_list = [9, 8, 3, 5, 4, 1, 8, 4, 1]
2
3 total = 0
4
5 for i in number_list
6       total += i
7 end
8
9 println("The total sum of the list is $(total)")
```

- Line 3: Defines the variable `total` and initialises it to 0.
- Line 5: Iterates through the length of the array, 1 to 9 (inclusive).
- Line 6: Takes the current value of total and adds the current value in the array to the total. This cumulative total is commonly used for scores and timers in programs.
- Another is also shown below:

```
1  function total_list(number_list_in)
2        total = 0
3
4        for i in number_list_in
5              total += i
6        end
7        return total
8  end
9
10 function main()
11       numbers_list = [9, 8, 3, 5, 4, 1, 8, 4, 1]
12
13       total_out = total_list(numbers_list)
14       println("The sum of the array is $(total_out)")
16 end
```

CHALLENGE 28: AVERAGE OF A LIST

Write a function called `mean_of_list` that takes a list of numbers as an argument and returns the mean.

Write the main function which contains your list and calls the `mean_of_list` function.

CHALLENGE 29: COUNTING VOWELS

Iterate through the sentence below and count how many times each vowel occurs. At the end of the program, ouput the number of As, Es, Is, Os and Us with a meaningful message.

sentence = "Learning programming is similar to learning a musical instrument. Both involve practise and making lots of mistakes. Both also require perseverance to develop fluency. Keep going!"

```
function counting_vowels(sentence)
```

```
    A = 0
```

```
    E = 0
```



```
    for
```

```
        letter = uppercase(letter)
```

```
        if letter == 'A'
```

LINEAR SEARCH IN A NESTED ARRAY

A program which searches for a student's results within a nested array of exam scores.

```
1   cs_scores=[["Jo", 45, 60 , 72 ],["Zi", 55 , 65 , 70 ],
2   ["Ellie", 71 , 78 , 78 ],["Jessica" , 68 , 79 , 80 ],
3   ["Taseen", 65 , 70 , 71 ]]
4
5   println("We will try to find the result for a given
6   student's exam")
7
8   println("Enter a student name: ")
9   name = readline()
10  println("Enter the exam number: ")
11  exam_number = parse(Int, readline())
12
13  found = false
14
15  for i in cs_scores
16      if name == i[1]
17          global found = true
18          result = i[exam_number + 1]
19          println("$(name)'s result for exam $(exam_number)
20  was $(result)")
21      end
22  end
23
24  if found == false
25      println("$(name) cannot be found")
26  end
```

- Lines 1-3: This is an array of arrays, also known as a nested array. Each element of the outer array is another array
- Line 13: Use a variable to set a Boolean flag to False.
- Lines 16-18: if the name is located, the found flag is set to True and the result can be found by indexing the nested array using the current count and the exam_number.
- Line 24: if we reach the end of the list and found is still False, then the number was not in the list.
- Lines 20 and 21: Output a meaningful message.

CHALLENGE 30: GRADE BOUNDARIES

An high-school student wants to find out how many marks are required to receive a certain grade. Write a function that takes a user's desired grade as an argument and then iterates through the nested array to return the number of marks they need for that grade.

function _____ (_____)

```
    boundaries = [["A*",  90], ["A", 83], ["B",
72], ["C", 60], ["D", 49], ["E", 30]]
```

CHALLENGE 31: COUNTING VOWELS USING A DICT

Use a dictionary to improve challenge 29; keeping track of how many times each vowel occurs in the sentence below. A dictionary or a hash table (known as a Dict in Julia) is a list of associations between names and values At the end of the program, ouput the number of A's, E's, I's, O's and U's.

sentence = "Learning programming is similar to learning a musical instrument. Both involve practise and making lots of mistakes. Both also require perseverance to develop fluency. Keep going!"

```
function counting_vowels(sentence)
        vowels = Dict('A' => 0, 'E' => 0, 'I'
=> 0, 'O' => 0, 'U' => 0)
```

TOTAL OF A NESTED ARRAY

A program which adds up each student's scores in a nested array
i.e. a row or sub list

```
1   cs_scores = [["Karman", 45, 60, 72],
2        ["Daniel", 55, 65, 70],
3        ["Parker", 71, 78, 78],
4        ["Jessica", 68, 79, 80],
5        ["Edie", 98, 85, 91]]
6
7   for student in cs_scores
8        total = 0
9        for exam in 2:4
10            total += student[exam]
11        end
12        println("Total for $(student[1]) = $total")
13        total = 0
14  end
```

- In the program above we are trying to calculate each student's
  total, so the student is in the first loop. This is also known as the
  outer loop.
- Line 8: Iterate through each student .
- Line 9: Now starting with student 1 i.e. Karman, enter the nested
  inner loop through exams 2 to 4 (inclusive) i.e. exams 1-3.
- Line 10: Add the score to the running total.
- Line 12: Output the student's total.

CHALLENGE 32: TOTAL FOR EACH EXAM IN A NESTED ARRAY

Write a program which will output the total for each exam with a meaningful message.

Hint: As the focus is on each *exam* rather than each student, the outer for loop will be for each *exam.* Remember to reset the total after each iteration of the inner loop.

```
cs_scores = [["Karman", 45, 60, 72],
    ["Daniel", 55, 65, 72],
    ["Parker", 71, 78, 78],
    ["Jessica", 68, 79, 80],
    ["Edie", 98, 85, 91]]


total = 0


for exam in
```

CHALLENGE 33: AVERAGE FOR EACH STUDENT IN A NESTED ARRAY

Write a program that outputs the mean average for each student.

Hint: Remember to reset the total to 0 after outputting the average for each student

```
cs_scores = [["Theo", 45, 60, 72],
      ["Angharad", 55, 65, 70],
      ["Sameer", 71, 78, 78],
      ["Adrian", 68, 79, 80],
      ["Ayana", 98, 85, 91]]
```

CHALLENGE 34: AVERAGE FOR EACH STUDENT IN A NESTED ARRAY

Re-write challenge 33 so that it is a function. The function should take the nested array of exam results as an argument and output the mean average for each student.

```
cs_scores = [["Theo", 45, 60, 72],
    ["Angharad", 55, 65, 70],
    ["Sameer", 71, 78, 78],
    ["Adrian", 68, 79, 80],
    ["Ayana", 98, 85, 91]]
```

CHALLENGE 35: TRACING LOOPS

1) Write the values of x and y for the first 5 iterations of the program below:

x	y	output
0		

```
1    animals = [["Charlie", "Dog", 8],
2               ["Dolly", "Sheep", 3],
3               ["Wanda", "Goldfish", 4]]
4
5    for x in 1:size(animals, 1)
6         for y in 1:3
7              println(animals[x][y])
8         end
9    end
```

2) What is the name of the data structure on lines 1-3?

_____

3) The Nested for loop on line 5-7 is an example of which programming construct?

A.   Sequence

B.   Selection

C.   Iteration

CHALLENGE 36: MULTIPLE CHOICE QUESTIONS

Circle the correct answer based on the following code:

```
for x in 1:3
    for y in 2:4
        z = x + y
        println(z)
    end
end
```

1) What is output when the program above is run?

A.   0,1,2,2,3,4

B.   2,3,4,5,3,4,5,6,3,4,5,6

C.   0,1,2,3,2,3,4,5

D.   2,3,4,5,6,3,4,5,6,7,4,5,6,7,8,5,6,7,8,

2) Given the code in Challenge 35 and given that
`print(animals[2][3])` gives the output of 3. What does
`print(animals[3][1])` output?

A.   3, 0

B.   4

C.   Wanda

D.   Dolly

3) Referring again to challenge 35, what would be output if the
following code was run `print(animals[4][4])`

A.   3, 3

B.   Bounds error

C.   Syntax error

D.   Index error: list index out of range

JULIA PACKAGES

Packages are a way to extend the capability of a programming language. To add packages to your device, go to the Julia terminal and type in a square bracket (']'). This should change the prompt from `julia>` to `(@1.5) pkg>`. Then, type in `add <package name>`, which will install the package to your computer permanently. To use it in each Julia instance, use `using <package name>`, allowing you to use that package's features. Examples of widely used packages are Colors, IJulia, Plots and Flux.

USING CSV TO READ TEXT FILES

A common way of structuring .txt files and reading them is using CSV formatting, or Comma Separated Values. In Julia, this is done using the CSV package. The function used to read CSV files is the CSV.File function, which takes the filename string. This returns a CSV.File object, which is made up of rows which are similar to dicts as they have column names which correspond to values. In a CSV.Row, you use the column name to get a value

users.txt
``` username,password "LauW", "insecurePwd" "VegaJ", "iLoveWebDesign" "LassamiL", "zeroDawn" ```

LOGIN SYSTEM BY READING CSV IN A .TXT FILE

A function which performs a linear search on data that is stored in a CSV file. See previous page for users.txt file.

```
1    using CSV
2
3    function login()
4        println("What is your username?")
5        username_in = readline()
6        println("What is your password?")
7        password_in = readline()
8        users = CSV.File("users.txt")
9        found = false
10       for user in users
11           if username_in == user.username
12               found = true
13               if password_in == user.password
14                   println("Logged in")
15               else
16                   println("Incorrect password")
17                   login()
18               end
19           end
20       end
21       if found == false
22           println("Invalid username")
23           login()
24       end
25   end
26
27   login()
```

- Lines 4-7: Take the user's input for their file
- Line 8: Read the file users.txt using CSV.File. The CSV.File object is stored in the variable users.
- Line 10: Each user in the for loop is a CSV.Row object
- Lines 10-17: Loop through the CSV.File to find the valid user and login.
- Lines 17 and 23: calls the `login` function if the login fails i.e. it restarts the function.

CHALLENGE 37: UNIQUE USERNAME

Write a function which generates a username for a teacher based on their first name and surname. The format should be their surname, followed by the first letter of their first name. The program should check to see if the username already exists in users.txt and if so, a unique username should be generated by appending a "#" symbol. E.g. if a teacher joins the school called Winnie Lau, their username would be LauW# . The username should then be returned.

using CSV

```
function generate_username(firstname, lastname)
    username = _____


    #check to see if the username already exists
    users = _____("users.txt")
    found = false
    for user in users




```

CHALLENGE 38: USING THE UNIQUE USERNAME FUNCTION

Write a program which asks for a teacher's first name and surname. Then demonstrate how you would call the function on the previous page to generate a username and output this in a meaningful message.

The next page is provided so that you can practise Challenge 37 again without the prompt. It's important that you keep challenging yourself and eventually you should be able to write these programs independently.

CHALLENGE 37: UNIQUE USERNAME

Write a function which generates a username for a teacher based on their first name and surname. The format should be their surname, followed by the first letter of their first name. The program should check to see if the username already exists in users.txt and if so, a unique username should be generated by appending a "#" symbol. E.g. if a teacher joins the school called Winnie Lau, their username would be LauW# . The username should then be returned.

WRITING A SHOPPING LIST TO A FILE

File writing is essential if you want to save data permanently to your programs. This allows you to open a program and read in data. Examples of data might be a shopping list, usernames and passwords, player names and scores. The program below asks a user for shopping list items to be written to a file which stores an Type this out to check if a shopping_list.txt file is created next to your Julia file and to check if your shopping list is written there.

```
1   function shopping()
2       items = []
3       while true
4           println("Enter an item or 'End' to finish the
5   list.")
6           item = titlecase(readline())
7           if item == "End"
8               break
9           else
10              push!(items, item)
11          end
12      end
13      f = open("shoppinglist.txt", "w")
14      write(f, string(items))
15      close(f)
16  end
17
18  shopping()
```

- Line 2: Creates an empty array which will append to on line 10
- Lines 4-6: Allows the user to keep entering items and casts their item to title case i.e. capital letter on the first character.
- Lines 7-10: Checks if the item is "End" and if not, it appends the item to the items array. If it is "End", the while loop is stopped using the break keyword
- Line 9: Opens a file in write mode. If one does not exist, it will create a new file. If it already exists, it will overwrite the content.
- Line 14: Writes the array as a string into the file.

ADDING TO A LIST IN A FILE

On the previous page, we learnt that opening a file in write mode will erase the previous data if the file already exists. There are two ways of adding to an existing file. However, when we are dealing with lists in Julia, a simple approach is to read in a list from the file, append to the list and then overwrite the file with this updated list. This is shown below.

Shopping_list.txt
['Rice', 'Ackee', 'Peppers', 'Tomatoes']

```
1   function add_shopping()
2       shopping_list = evalfile(joinpath(pwd(),
3   "shoppinglist.txt"), [])
4       while true
5           println("Enter a shopping list item or enter 'End'
6   to finish your list.")
7           item = titlecase(readline())
8
9           if item == "End"
10              break
11          else
12              push!(shopping_list, item)
13          end
14      end
15
16      f = open("shoppinglist.txt", "w")
17      write(f, string(shopping_list))
18      close(f)
19  end
```

We have only changed a few lines, these evaluate the contents of the file into an array called shopping_list.

If you have paired sets of data e.g. player names and scores or usernames and passwords, you may want to use CSV format in a file. The rest of the code stays the same. However, it's worth noting that storing the password as plaintext may be fine for simple examples, but in real applications, it is a really bad idea!

CHALLENGE 39: REGISTER AN ACCOUNT

Write a function to allow a teacher to register a new account. The function should take the username and password as arguments and write these details to the existing users.txt file shown earlier.

Hint: Use the comments on the next page as skeleton code to structure your function.

```
function new_user(username_in, password_in)

    user = _____


    f = open(_____ , "a")
    write(f, _____ )
```

CHALLENGE 39: REGISTER AN ACCOUNT CONTINUED...

users.txt
username,password "LauW", "insecurePwd" "VegaJ", "iLoveWebDesign" "LassamiL", "zeroDawn"

define a function new_user with two parameters:
username and password

_____

concatenate the inputted strings to form the CSV row
format of the new user — "Username", "Password"

_____

_____

open the file in append mode using "a" as the second
object of open()

_____

write the user to the file

_____

close the file

_____

_____

_____

_____

_____

_____

_____

CHALLENGE 40: MULTIPLE CHOICE QUESTIONS

1) To append to the end of a file we should use?

A.   `file.append("some text")`

B.   `file = open("txtfile.txt", "a")`
      `write(file, "some text")`

C.   `file = open("txtfile.txt", "append")`
      `append(file, "some text")`

D.   `file = "some text".append()`

2) Opening a file in "w" mode will usually...:

A.   Allow you to write to a file, wiping the original data
B.   Allow you to write to the end of a file
C.   Allow you to write to the beginning of a file, keeping what is there
D.   Allow you to read or write from the file

3) After file operations, we should always

A.   Close the file
B.   Save the file with a new file name
C.   Loop back to the beginning of the file
D.   Open the file

CHALLENGE 41: PARSON'S PUZZLE

Solve the puzzle by re-arranging the code blocks into the correct order. The program should ask for a user's e-mail address and if it is in the nested array stored in the file, it returns True otherwise it returns False.

A
```
users = evalfile(joinpath(pwd(), "users.txt"))
```

B
```
println("Enter a username")
email = readline()
```

C
```
for user in users
```

D
```
return found
```

E
```
        if email == user
            found = true
```

F
```
found = false
```

Correct order:

66

CONVERTING BINARY TO DENARY

A function which takes a 4-bit binary string as an argument and returns the denary equivalent

```
1  function binary_to_denary(binary)
2      bit1 = parse(Int, binary[4]) * 1
3      bit2 = parse(Int, binary[3]) * 2
4      bit3 = parse(Int, binary[2]) * 4
5      bit4 = parse(Int, binary[1]) * 8
6
7      denary_out = bit1 + bit2 + bit3 + bit4
8      return denary_out
9  end
10
11 function main()
12     println("Enter the binary string")
13     binary_in = readline()
14     denary = binary_to_denary(binary_in)
15     println("Binary $(binary_in) in denary is $(denary)")
16 end
17
18 main()
19
```

- Line 12: Asks the user for a binary string.
- Line 13: Calls the `binary_to_denary` function, passing the binary string as an argument. The returned value will be stored in the denary variable and output on Line 14.
- Line 1: Defines a function called `binary_to_denary` and takes the `binary_in` string as an argument.
- Lines 2-5: Slices each individual digit and multiplies it by its relevant place value.
- Lines 7-8: The total is calculated and returned.
- Line 14: The denary equivalent is outputted with a meaningful message.

CONVERTING DENARY TO BINARY

A program which converts a denary value between 0-15 to a 4-bit binary value

```
1   println("Enter the denary number between 0 and 15")
2   denary = parse(Int, readline())
3
4   binary = ["0","0","0","0"]
5
6   if denary > 15
7       error("The number must be less then 15")
8   end
9   if denary >= 8 && denary <= 15
10      binary[1] = "1"
11      denary = denary - 8
12  end
13  if denary >= 4
14      binary[2] = "1"
15      denary = denary - 4
16  end
17  if denary >= 2
18      binary[3] = "1"
19      denary = denary - 2
20  end
21  if denary >= 1
22      binary[4] = "1"
23  end
24
25
26  for i in binary
27      print(i)
28  end
```

- Line 4: With binary numbers, we cannot use the integer data type. A default string of "0000" also cannot be used as strings in Julia are not mutable. Having four bits like the previous program could work, but you would have to define and initialise each bit. This could create up to four lines of extra code. It is therefore best to use a array as array are mutable.
- Lines 9-22: This models the "left-to-right" process of checking how many 8s, 4s, 2s and 1s go into a number between 0-15.
- Lines 26-27: This is a way to iterate through the list and print each element without commas, brackets and new lines.

CHALLENGE 42: CONVERTING HEXADECIMAL TO DENARY

Write a function which takes in 1 hexadecimal digit as an argument and returns the denary equivalent.

Write a main function which asks the user to input a hexadecimal value and then passes this value to the function you have written.

CHALLENGE 43: A COMPUTER SCIENCE QUIZ

Q1) What is the correct answer in Q1 below? Fill in the gap in the if statement on line 25

```
1   function correct(score_in)
2       println("Well done, this is the correct answer")
3       score_in += 1
4       return score_in
5   end
6
7   function quiz()
8       score = 0
9
10      println("""
11      Why do computers need primary storage?
12
13      A) To provide fast access memory to the CPU in the form
14  of RAM and ROM
15      B) To provide long term storage of files on a hard disk
16  drive
17      C) To act as RAM and allow programs to keep running when
18  RAM is full
19      D) To provide storage in case secondary storage runs out
20      """)
21
22      println("Choose a letter")
23      Q1 = uppercase(readline())
24
25      if Q1 == "__"
26          score = correct(score)
27          println(score)
28      end
29  end
```

Q2) When the program is run, nothing happens. Explain why?

_____

_____

Q3) What is the purpose of line 8?

_____

_____

CHALLENGE 44: BINARY SEARCH

Examine the binary search program below.

```
1    # Binary search returns location of target in given
2    # list if present, else returns -1
3    function binarySearch(nums, target)
4        left = 1
5        right = length(nums)
6        while left <= right
7
8            mid = left + (right - left) ÷ 2
9
10           # Check if target is present at mid
11           if nums[mid] == target
12               return mid
13
14           # If x is greater, ignore left half
15           elseif nums[mid] < target
16               left = mid + 1
17
18           # If x is smaller, ignore right half
19           else
20               right = mid - 1
21
22       # If we reach here, then the element was
23       # not present
24       return -1
25   end
26
27   nums_in = [2, 3, 4, 10, 40]
28   println("Enter a number to see if it is in the list")
29   target_in = parse(Int, readline())
30   result = binarySearch(nums_in, target_in)
31
32   if result != -1
33       println("Element is present at index $(result)")
34   else
35       println("Element is not present in array")
36   end
```

CHALLENGE 44: BINARY SEARCH CONTINUED...

Q1) What line is the function called on?

Q2) What is the name of the data structure on line 27?

Q3) How many parameters does the binarySearch function have?

Q4) When the program is run and the target_in is 10, what is the output?

Q5) When the program is run and the target_in is 20, what is the output?

Q6) The ÷ on line 8 is a floor division operator. Explain what is meant by floor division.

Q7) What is the type of target_in on line 29?

CHALLENGE 45: STORE DISCOUNT

Examine the program below which is used to issue store discount.

```
1    discounts = [["summer10", 0.1],
2                 ["welcome", 0.15],
3                 ["refer20", 0.2]]
4
5    discount = 0
6
7    println("What is the order total: £")
8    total = parse(Float64, readline())
9    println("Do you have a discount code?")
10   discount_in = lowercase(readline())
11
12   if discount_in == "yes"
13       println("Enter a discount code")
14       discountcode = lowercase(readline())
15
16       valid = false
17
18       for i in discounts
19           if discountcode == i[1]
20               global discount = i[2]
21               global valid = true
22           end
23       end
24
25       if valid == false
26           println("Invalid discount code")
27       end
28   end
29
30   total = total - total * discount
31   println("Your total is £$(total)")
```

CHALLENGE 45: STORE DISCOUNT CONTINUED...

Q1) Re-write the nested array to include another discount code called "loyalty25" worth 25% off.

Q2) What is the type of the variable `valid`?

Q3) Assume your nested array in Q1 is now stored in a text file called "`codes.txt`". What would you need to write between lines 15-19 so that the discount codes are read from the text file?

Q4) The program could be re-written using functions. Explain the advantages of using functions.

CHALLENGE 46: BUBBLE SORT SNIPPET

A bubble sort iterates through an array (or list) of numbers from left to right. If the number being checked is greater than the next item in the array, the numbers are swapped. One way of achieving this is by storing the first number in a temporary vaiable.

Part of the bubble sort is shown below. `j` is a variable in a nested for loop which allows the algorithm to iterate over the length of the `nums` array.

```
1     nums = [9, 1, 12, 3, 4, 8]
...
15    if nums[j] > nums[j + 1]
16        temp = nums[j]
17        nums[j] = nums[j + 1]
18        nums[j + 1] = nums[j]
19    end
```

The nums list can be visualised below:

nums[j]	nums[j+1]				
9	1	12	3	4	8

Q1) After the program runs, what is the value of temp?

Q2) In the above scenario, what are the final values of nums[j] and nums[j+1]? Explain whether the bubble sort has worked for the first two items?

CHALLENGE 46 BUBBLE SORT SNIPPET CONTINUED...

Q3) What is the name of the programming construct shown in the program:

A.   Sequence
B.   Selection
C.   Iteration

Q4) Give the name of two variables in the bubble sort snippet:

Q5) Name another sorting algorithm which might be more effective on a larger data set:

Q6) Explain why you might use a bubble sort instead of a different sorting algorithm:

CHALLENGE 47: CALCULATING THE FILE SIZE OF A TEXT FILE

The size of a text file can be calculated by using the following formula:

File size = bits per character * number of characters

Q1) Write a function which takes the bits per character and number of characters as parameters and returns the file size in kilobytes.

Q2) ASCII is a character set which always uses 8 bits per character

If a text file encoded using ASCII has 1000 characters. How many bits will the file size be?

Q3) Text is always stored as binary. ASCII has 8 bits and therefore can represent 2^8 characters. Some formats of Unicode use 32 bits per character. This would create larger file sizes. Explain why you might want to use Unicode instead of ASCII?

CHALLENGE 47: CALCULATING THE FILE SIZE OF A TEXT FILE CONTINUED...

Q4) The file size returned will be given in bits, therefore we can convert this to Kilobytes by dividing the answer by (8 * 1000.)

Use the space below to show how the function may be called. The answer should be outputted in KB.

Q5) Give your answer to Q2 from the previous page in Kilobytes:

CHALLENGE 48: CALCULATING THE FILE SIZE OF A SOUND FILE

The size of a sound file can be calculated by using the following formula:

File size = sample rate * bit depth * duration

Write a function which takes the sample rate (a frequency measured in Hz), bit depth and duration (measured in seconds) of a sound file and returns the file size.

STATISTICS

Julia provides access to large amount of mathematical functionality. Some of these modules are included in base Julia, and others can be installed as separate packages. Statistics is one of the modules included in base Julia. It can be loaded into your program with the `using` keyword. The Statistics module can be used to do common statistical calculations on data.

Shown below is a function to calculate the average of each row of a 2D matrix.

```
1   using Statistics
2
3   cs_scores = [45 60 72;
4                55 65 72;
5                98 85 91]
6
7   function average(array)
8       avg_score = zeros(size(array, 1))
9       for i in 1:size(array, 1)
10          average = mean(array[i, :])
11          avg_score[i] = average
12      end
13      return avg_score
14  end
15
16  average(cs_scores)
```

- Line 3-5: Define a two-dimensional array (also known as a matrix). This is different from the nested arrays we saw. These are indexed by rows and columns: `array[r, c]`
- Line 8: `size(array, 1)` returns the number of rows, and `zeros()` creates of a array of that length.
- Line 10: `array[i,:]` gives all the columns of the `i`th row.
- Line 10: The `mean()` function calculates the average.

Statistics also includes several other useful functions such as: `std, var, median, middle` etc. As you learn more maths, you can start to work with more Julia packages, such as Calculus.jl and DifferentialEquations.jl

CHALLENGE 49: STANDARD DEVIATION

Write a function similar to the one seen on the last page that calculates the standard deviation (with the `std` function) of each row of a 2D matrix and returns the output as an array, with each one element for each row.

```
using Statistics
```

```
function standard_deviation(array)
```

PLOTTING

When you are working with data sets, it can be useful to visualize it using a graph in order to easily spot trends in the data. The easiest way to do this in Julia is using the Plots.jl package. For example:

```
plot(1:10,rand(1:10,10))
```

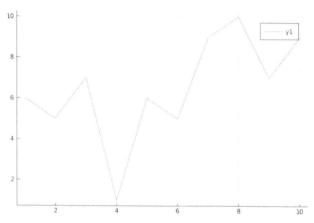

```
bar(1:10,rand(1:10,10))
```

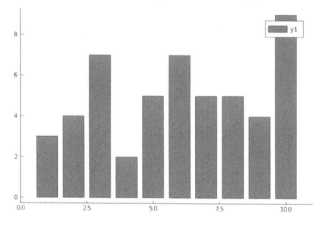

If you want to plot a new data series on top of a pre-existing graph, add an exclamation mark to the end of the function name:
```
plot!() or bar!().
```

CHALLENGE 50: PLOT STANDARD DEVIATION

Using the average and standard deviation functions, write a function that takes a vector of names and a matrix of scores and plots the mean (as a bar graph) and then plots the standard deviation on top of that.

```
using Statistics, Plots


cs_scores = ["Karman" 45 60 72;

             "Daniel" 55 65 72;

             "Parker" 71 78 78;

             "Jessica" 68 79 80;

             "Edie" 98 85 91]


names_in = cs_scores[:, 1]
scores_in = cs_scores[:, ____]
#Define average and standard deviation
function plot_scores(____, ____)
```

SOLUTIONS

There is always more than one way to solve a problem. Even if the algorithm is well-defined, there may be alternative programming approaches. The following pages present examples which you can compare to your own answers. Comments have been provided to aid your understanding, you should develop the habit of commenting all your programs.

CHALLENGES 1 AND 2:

```
#define a function called highest_num with three parameters
function highest_number(num1, num2, num3)
    # return the highest number
    if num1 >= num2 >= num3
        return num1
    elseif num2 >= num1 >= num3
        return num2
    else
        return num3
    end
end


println("Enter 1st number:")
num1 = parse(Int, readline())
println("Enter 2nd number:")
num2 = parse(Int, readline())
println("Enter 3rd number:")
num3 = parse(Int, readline())

#  call the highest_number function and pass the contents of
#  first, second and third variables as arguments into the
#  parameters num1, num2, num3
highest = highernum(num1, num2, num3)

#output the highest number with a meaningful message
println("The higher number was ", highest)
```

CHALLENGES 3 AND 4:

```
function options(num)
    if num == 1
        return "Computer Science"
    elseif num == 2
        return "Music"
    elseif num == 3
        return "Dance"
    elseif num == 4
        return "PE"
    else
        return "Error"
    end
end

println("""
1 Computer Science
2 Music
3 Dance
4 PE
""")
print("Enter option number: ")
opt_num = parse(Int, readline())
println("You chose " * options(opt_num))
```

CHALLENGE 5:

Q1)

num_in	Ouput
8	8
3	8
12	12
5	5

Q2) Lines 4-7

Q3) 3 is less than 5 so the first branch of the if statement is executed and the output is 8. The latter elseif num == 3 branch is never reached.

CHALLENGE 6:

```
function mystery_number(num)
    if num == 3
        println(1)
    elseif num < 5
        println(8)
    else
        println(num)
    end
end

println("Enter a number:")
num_in = parse(Int, readline())
mystery_number(num_in)
```

CHALLENGE 7:

```
# B, E, D, C, A

function subtract(num1, num2)
    if num1 > num2
        out = num1 - num2
    else
        out = num2 - num1
    end
    return out
end

println("Enter a number")
num1_in = parse(Int, readline())
println("Enter a number")
num2_in = parse(Int, readline())

difference = subtract(num1_in, num2_in)
println("The difference is ", difference)
```

CHALLENGE 8:

1) A/B Using return and Last computed value
2) C. if num1 is greater than 9
3) C. Arguments
4) D. function

CHALLENGE 9:

```
function initials_only(first, middle, last)
    initials = first[1] * middle[1] * last[1]
    return initials
end

println("What is your first name")
firstname = readline()
println("What is your middle name")
midname = readline()
println("What is your last name")
lastname = readline()

initials = initials_only(firstname, midname, lastname)
println("Your initials are: " * initials)
```

CHALLENGE 10:

```
function subject_shortener(subject)
    short = subject[1:3]
    return short
end

println("Enter the subject name")
subj = readline()
subj_out = subject_shortener(subj)
println("$(subj) has been shortened to $(subj_out)")
```

CHALLENGE 11:

```
function cuboid_volume(len, wid, hei)
    return len * wid * hei
end

println("Enter the length of the cuboid")
length_in = parse(Int, readline())
println("Enter the width of the cuboid")
width_in = parse(Int, readline())
println("Enter the height of the cuboid")
height_in = parse(Int, readline())

volume = cuboid_volume(length_in, width_in, height_in)
println("Volume is $(volume)")
```

CHALLENGE 12:

```
add(num1, num2) = num1 + num2

println("Enter a number")
num1_in = parse(Int, readline())
println("Enter another number")
num2_in = parse(Int, readline())

total = add(num1_in, num2_in)

println("The sum of the two numbers is $(total)")
```

CHALLENGE 13:

1) B. ena
2) A. C
3) D. 8
4) B. A value which can not change whilst the program is running

CHALLENGE 14:

```
function is_odd(num)
    if num % 2 == 0
        return "even"
    else
        return "odd"
    end
end

while true
    println("Enter a number or STOP to finish")
    number = parse(Int, readline())

    if number != "STOP"
        odd = is_odd(number)
    else
        break
    end
end
```

CHALLENGE 15:

```
function is_multiple(x_in, y_in)
    if x % y == 0
        println("$(x) is a multiple of $(y)")
    else
        println("$(x) is not a multiple of $(y)")
    end
end

println("A program to check if x is a multiple of y")
println("Enter a number to see if it is a multiple")
x = parse(Int, readline())
println("Enter a number to divide by")
y = parse(Int, readline())
is_multiple(x, y)
```

CHALLENGE 16:

Q1)

num1	num2	Output
1	8	0
3	9	1
14	10	2
21	19-28	4

Q2)

a) 21 DIV 7 = 3
b) 9 DIV 4 = 2

CHALLENGE 17:

```
sentinel = "XXX"
acronym = ""
while true
    println("Enter a word or 'XXX' to finish")
    word = readline()
    if word != sentinel
        global acronym = acronym * word[1]
    else
        break
    end
end

println(acronym)
```

CHALLENGE 18:

```
acronym = ""

println("Enter words to convert to acronym")

words = readline()

Words_list = split(words)

for word in words_list
    global acronym
    acronym = acronym * word[1]
end

println(acronym)
```

CHALLENGE 19:

```
while true
    x = rand(1:6)
    y = rand(1:6)
    println("$(x), $(y)")
    if x != y
        println("Press enter to keep rolling")
        readline()
    else
        println("Game loading...")
        break
    end
end
```

CHALLENGE 20:

```
sum = 0

for i in 1:3
    global sum
    x = rand(1:6)
    y = dice_roll()
    println("$(x), $(y)")
    println("Total for Round $(i): $(x + y)")
    sum += x + y
end

println("Total for all three rounds: $(sum)")
```

CHALLENGE 21:

```
numbers = [9, 8, 72, 22, 21, 81, 2, 1, 11, 76, 32, 54]
highest = numbers[1]

for i in numbers
    global highest
    if highest < i
        highest = i
    end
end

print("The highest number is ", highest)
```

CHALLENGE 22:

```
numbers = [9, 8, 72, 22, 21, 81, 2, 1, 11, 76, 32, 54]

function highest_num(numbers_in)
    max = 0
    for number in numbers_in
        if number > max
            max = number
        end
    end
    return max
end

highest_out = highest_num(numbers)
println("The highest number is $(highest_out)")
```

CHALLENGES 23 AND 24:

```
function weak_password(password)
    weak_passwords = ["password", "qwerty", "hello123",
"letmein", "123456"]
    for pass in weak_passwords
        if password == pass
            println("WEAK: Weak password")
            return Nothing
        end
    end
    is_num = false
    uppercase = false
    lowercase = false
    for char in password
        if isnumeric(char)
            is_num = true
        elseif isuppercase(char)
            uppercase = true
        elseif islowercase(char)
            lowercase = true
        end
    end
    if is_num == false
        println("WEAK: No numerics")
    elseif length(password) < 8
        println("WEAK: Too short")
    elseif uppercase == false
        println("WEAK: No uppercase letters")
    elseif lowercase == false
        println("WEAK: No lowercase letters")
    end
end
```

CHALLENGE 25:

```
keeper = [rand(["left", "centre", "right"]) for i in 1:5]
shots_in = 0

for i in keeper
    global shots_in
    println("Type in shot direction (left, centre, right)")
    shot = readline()
    if i == shot
        println("Saved!")
    else
        println("Goal!")
        shots_in += 1
    end
end

println("You scored $(shots_in) and missed $(5 - shots_in)")
```

CHALLENGE 26:

1)

x	y
0	2
1	2
2	4
3	4

2) for x in 1:10

CHALLENGE 27:

Circle the correct answer based on the following code:

```
for count in 1:5
    num1 = rand(1:10)
end
```

1) A. 10 and 1
2) B. 0 and 4
3) A. 5 times

4) `for words in sentence`
or `for count in length(sentence)`

CHALLENGE 28:

```
function mean_of_list(num_list)
    sum = 0
    for x in num_list
        sum += x
    end
    mean = sum / length(num_list)
    return mean
end

function main()
    numbers_list = [0,7,5,3,22,23,11,34,51,32,5,3,1]

    mean = mean_of_list(numbers_list)
    println("The mean average of $numbers_list = $mean")
end

main()
```

CHALLENGE 29:

```
function vowel_counter(sentence)
    A = 0
    E = 0
    I = 0
    O = 0
    U = 0
    for letter in sentence
        letter = uppercase(letter)
        if letter == 'A'
            A += 1
        elseif letter == 'E'
            E += 1
        elseif letter == 'I'
            I += 1
        elseif letter == 'O'
            O += 1
        elseif letter == 'U'
            U += 1
        end
    end
    println("Number of A's: $A")
    println("Number of E's: $E")
    println("Number of I's: $I")
    println("Number of O's: $O")
    println("Number of U's: $U")
end

sentence = "Learning programming is similar to learning a
musical instrument. Both involve practise and making lots of
mistakes. Both also require perseverance to develop fluency.
Keep going!"

vowel_counter(sentence)
```

CHALLENGE 30:

```
function grade_boundaries(desired_grade)
    boundaries = [["A*",  90], ["A", 83], ["B", 72], ["C",
60], ["D", 49], ["E", 30]]
    for grade in boundaries
        if desired_grade == grade[1]
            return grade[2]
        end
    end
end

println("What grade do you wish to achieve:")
grade = readline()
mark = grade_boundaries(grade)
prinln("Grade boudary for $grade is $mark")
```

CHALLENGE 31:

```
function counting_vowels(sentence)
    vowels = Dict('A' ⇒ 0, 'E' ⇒ 0, 'I' ⇒ 0, 'O' ⇒ 0, 'U'
⇒ 0)
    for letter in sentence
        letter = uppercase(letter)
        if letter == 'A' || letter == 'E' || letter == 'I' ||
letter == 'O' || letter == 'U'
            vowels[letter] += 1
        end
    end
    for vowel in vowels
        println(vowel)
    end
end

sentence = "Learning programming is similar to learning a
musical instrument. Both involve practise and making lots of
mistakes. Both also require perseverance to develop fluency.
Keep going!"

counting_vowels(sentence)
```

CHALLENGE 32:

```
cs_scores = [["Karman", "45", "60", "72"], ["Daniel", "55",
"65", "72"], ["Parker", "71", "78", "78"], ["Jessica", "68",
"79", "80"], ["Edie", "98", "85", "91"]]

total = 0

for exam in 2:4
    global total
    total = 0
    for student in cs_scores
        total += parse(Int, student[exam])
    end
    println("Total for Exam $(exam - 1) is $(total)")
end
```

CHALLENGE 33:

```
cs_scores = [["Theo", 45, 60, 72], ["Angharad", 55, 65, 70],
["Sameer", 71, 78, 78], ["Adrian", 68, 79, 80], ["Ayana", 98,
85, 91]]

for student in cs_scores
    total = 0
    for grade in student[2:4]
        total += grade
    end
    println("$(student[1])'s average was $(total/(length
(student) - 1))%")
end
```

CHALLENGE 34:

```
cs_scores = [["Theo", 45, 60, 72], ["Angharad", 55, 65, 70],
["Sameer", 71, 78, 78], ["Adrian", 68, 79, 80], ["Ayana", 98,
85, 91]]

function average_score(scores::Array{T}) where T <: Array
    for student in cs_scores
        total = 0
        for grade in student[2:4]
            total += grade
        end
        println("$(student[1])'s average was $(total/(length
(student) - 1))%")
    end
end

average_score(cs_scores)
```

CHALLENGE 35:

1)

x	y	output
0	0	Charlie
0	1	Dog
0	2	8
1	0	Dolly
1	1	Sheep

2) nested array

3) C. Iteration

CHALLENGE 36:

1) B 2,3,4,5,3,4,5,6,3,4,5,6
2) C Wanda
3) D Index error: list index out of range

CHALLENGES 37 AND 38:

```
using CSV

function generate_username(firstname, lastname)
    new_username = lastname * firstname[1]

    users = CSV.File("users.txt")

    found = false
    for user in users
        if new_username == user.username
            found = true
        end
    end

    if found == true
        new_username = new_username * "#"
    end
    return new_username
end

println("What is your first name?")
fname = readline()
println("What is your surname?")
sname = readline()
generate_username(fname, sname)
```

CHALLENGE 39:

```
function new_user(username_in, password_in)

    user = '"' * username_in * '"' * ", " * '"' * password_in *
'"'

    # Or, you can use the repr() function to add the speech marks
to the strings
    # user = repr(username_in) * ", " * repr(password_in)

    f = open("users.txt", "a")
    write(f, user)
    close(f)
end
```

CHALLENGE 40

1) B
file = open("txtfile.txt", "a")
write(file, "some text")

2) A Allow you to write to a file, wiping the original data

3) A Close the file

CHALLENGE 41

B
```
println("Enter a username")
email = readline()
```

A
```
evalfile(joinpath(pwd(), "users.txt"))
```

F
```
found = false
```

C
```
for user in users
```

E
```
    if email == user[1]
        found = true
```

F
```
return found
```

Correct order:

B	A	F	C	E	F

CHALLENGE 42

```
function hex_to_denary(hex)
    hex = hex[1]
    if isnumeric(hex)
        return hex
    elseif hex == 'a'
        return 10
    elseif hex == 'b'
        return 11
    elseif hex == 'c'
        return 12
    elseif hex == 'd'
        return 13
    elseif hex == 'e'
        return 14
    elseif hex == 'f'
        return 15
    end
end

function main()
    println("Enter the hexadecimal digit.")
    hexadecimal = readline()
    println(hex_to_denary(hexadecimal))
end
```

CHALLENGE 43

1) A

2) quiz() function has not been called

3) Declare a variable called score and initialise it to 0 so that we can keep track of the score by passing it into the correct function on line 26

CHALLENGE 44

1) 30

2) Array

3) 2

4) Element is present at index 4

5) Element is not present in array

6) Integer division or floor division. A division where you ignore the remainder and round down.

7) Int

CHALLENGE 45

1)
```
discounts = [["summer10",0.1],
             ["welcome",0.15],
             ["refer20",0.2],
             ["loyalty25",0.25]]
```

2) Boolean

3)
```
evalfile(joinpath(pwd(), "codes.txt")
```

4)
- Functions can be called anywhere in the program.
- Functions reduce the number of lines of code i.e. creates shorter programs.
- The programs are also more manageable as errors or changes to one function means you only make the change or the correction in one place, not several places throughout the program.

4 continued)

- Multiple people can work on the program, each working on a different function.
- The functions can be tested in isolation.
- Functions can be re-used in other programs and also imported .

CHALLENGE 46

1) Based on the snippet shown, nums[j] is 9 and this is stored in temp.

2) nums[j] and nums[j+1] both equal 1. The bubble sort has not worked. Line 18 should be nums[j+1] = temp. This ensures the original value of nums[j] i.e. 9 is stored in temp and then copied to nums[j]. The code as it stands first replaces nums[j] with 1 then replaces the value of nums[j+1] with the updated value of nums[j].

3) Selection

4) Any two from: temp, j and swapped

5) Insertion sort or merge sort

6) It uses little memory and is not processor intensive. If the array to be sorted is short or mostly already sorted, a bubble sort will be quicker to program and potentially quicker to run than an insertion sort or merge sort. These other sorting algorithms scale better i.e. they are suited for larger data sets,:

CHALLENGE 47

1)
```
function filesize(bitsperchar, num_chars)
    return bitsperchar * num_chars
end
```

2) 8 * 1000 = 8000 bits

3) More characters can be represented (2^{32}) in Unicode. Unicode includes emojis and non-English characters such as Japanese and Chinese.

4)
```
function main()
    println("Enter the number of bits per character:")
    bits = parse(Int, readline())

    println("Enter the number of characters:")
    characht = parse(Int, readline())

    size_b = filesize(bits, characht)
    size_kb = size_b / (8 * 1000)

    println("The file size is $size_kb KB")
end
```

5) 1KB

CHALLENGE 48

```
function filesize(sample_rate, bit_depth, duration)
    return sample_rate * bit_depth * duration
end

function main()
    println("Enter the frequency in Hz:")
    freq = parse(Int, readline())
    println("Enter the bit depth: ")
    bit_depth = parse(Int, readline())
    println("Enter the duration of the sound file in
seconds:")
    length = parse(Int, readline())

    size_out = filesize(freq, bit_depth, length)
    size_kb = size_out / (8 * 1000)
    size_mb = size_kb / 1000
    println("The file size is $size_kb KB")
    println("The file size is $size_mb MB")
end
```

CHALLENGE 49

```
function standard_deviation(array)
    scores_deviation = zeros(5)
    for i in 1:size(array)[1]
        deviation = std(array[i, :])
        scores_deviation[i] = deviation
    end
    return scores_deviation
end
```

CHALLENGE 50

```
using Plots, Statistics

cs_scores = ["Karman" 45 60 72;
             "Daniel" 55 65 72;
             "Parker" 71 78 78;
             "Jessica" 68 79 80;
             "Edie" 98 85 91]

names_in = cs_scores[:, 1]
scores_in = cs_scores[:, 2:4]

function average(array)
    avg_score = zeros(5)
    for i in 1:size(array)[1]
        average = mean(array[i, :])
        avg_score[i] = average
    end
    return avg_score
end

function standard_deviation(array)
    scores_deviation = zeros(5)
    for i in 1:size(array)[1]
        deviation = std(array[i, :])
        scores_deviation[i] = deviation
    end
    return scores_deviation
end

function plot_scores_avg(names, scores)
    bar(names, average(scores), label="Average Score",
ylims=(0,100))
    plot!(cs_scores[:,1], standard_deviation(scores),
label="Standard Deviation")
end
```

APPENDIX

To download Julia, visit the JuliaLang website at:
`https://julialang.org`, and click the "Download" link. Once
you download Julia, and run the installer. You will get
a `julia` binary in the *bin* directory where your install lives. Running
that program will leave you in a textual prompt, which is usually
called a REPL - Read-Eval-Print-Loop. You may want to install an
IDE — integrated development environment — such as Visual
Studio Code.

```
               |  Documentation: https://docs.julialang.org
   _       _ _ |
  (_)     | (_)|  Type "?" for help, "]?" for Pkg help.
   _ _   _| |_ __ _  |
  | | | | | | |/ _` | |  Version 1.5.0 (2020-08-01)
  | | |_| | | | (_| | |  Official https://julialang.org/ release
 _/ |\__'_|_|_|\__'_| |
|__/                  |

julia> function lower_num(num1, num2)
           if num1 <= num2
               lowest = num1
           else
               lowest = num2
           end
           return lowest
       end
lower_num (generic function with 1 method)

julia> lower_num(5,6)
5

julia>
```

FURTHER READING

Github repository– littlebookofalgorithms.jl	Ahan Sengupta
Github repository– JuliaByExample	Samuel Colvin
Julia Documentation	Julia community
Tanmay Teaches Julia for Beginners: A Springboard to Machine Learning for All Ages	Tanmay Bakshi
Think Julia	Ben Lauwens, Allen B. Downey
Julia Academy– Free courses to learn Julia and its packages	Julia community
Youtube channel– JuliaLang	Julia community
GameZero.jl– Simple game development in Julia	Avik Sengupta & Ahan Sengupta